All Together Now!

Poems by Tony Bradman

Illustrated by Julie Park

PUFFIN BOOKS

For Nick and Jenny

PUFFIN BOOKS

Published by the Penguin Group
Penguin Books Ltd, 27 Wrights Lane, London W8 5TZ, England
Viking Penguin, a division of Penguin Books USA Inc.
375 Hudson Street, New York, New York 10014, USA
Penguin Books Australia Ltd, Ringwood, Victoria, Australia
Penguin Books Canada Ltd, 2801 John Street, Markham, Ontario, Canada L3R 1B4
Penguin Books (NZ) Ltd, 182–190 Wairau Road, Auckland 10, New Zealand

Penguin Books Ltd, Registered Offices: Harmondsworth, Middlesex, England

First published by Viking Kestrel 1989
Published in Puffin Books 1990
10 9 8 7 6 5 4 3 2 1

Text copyright © Tony Bradman, 1989
Illustrations copyright © Julie Park, 1989
All rights reserved

Printed in England by Clays Ltd, St Ives plc
Filmset in Century Schoolbook (Linotron 202)

Contents

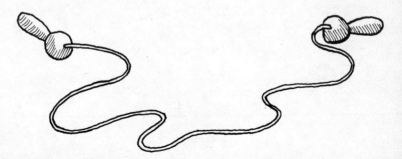

Kiss Me Quick

Kiss me quick, mum,
I can't wait,
My friend is standing
At the gate.

Kiss me quick, mum,
I must fly,
All my friends
Are going by.

Kiss me quick, mum,
Don't be slow . . .
I must be off now –
Cheerio!

This is the Mum

This is the mum
Who wakes me up
And gets me out of bed

This is the mum
Who helps me pull
My clean vest over my head

This is the mum
Who irons my clothes
Who puts out my clean socks

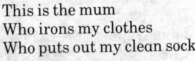

This is the mum
Who puts my lunch
Inside my new lunchbox

This is the mum
Who goes to work
Who tries not to be late

This is the mum
Who stands in the rain
By the infant gate

This is the mum
Who later on
Is there to make my tea

This is the mum
Who's looking tired
And occasionally

This is the mum
Who tells me off
For gobbling my food

This is the mum
Who loses her temper
When I'm being rude

This is the mum
Who loves me
At least that's what she said

And this is the mum
Who's telling me
To get myself to bed

13

In a Little Dream

My name's Helen
My mum says I'm a dreamer
She says my mind's
Always on other things
She gets cross
And says I'm always
In a little dream

I come out of school
Without my lunchbox
I forget my coat
I forget my book-bag
My mum gets cross
And says I'm always
In a little dream

14

I eat my dinner slowly
Because I stop and stare
And sometimes I even
Forget my dinner's there
My mum gets cross
And says I'm always
In a little dream

My name's Helen
My mum says I'm a dreamer
She says one day
I'll forget myself
She gets cross
And says . . . I forget
What she says . . .
I'm
In
A
Little
Dream . . .

Lazy

People say I'm lazy,
But I don't think I am.

I might lie in bed all day,
but I do my exercises.

Lift one eyebrow . . . oof!
Now the other . . . phew!
That was hard work!

And I do plenty of breathing.
Watch my chest. It's always
Going in, and out, in and out . . .

So when people call me lazy,
(It happens nearly every day)
This is all I've got to say –

Zzzzzzzzzzzzzzzzzzzzzzzzzz . . .

16

The Wedding

Today I'm being a bridesmaid,
I'm wearing a dress that's blue,
I've got a big bunch of flowers
And a pair of new, shiny shoes.

Everyone's feeling excited,
It's such a wonderful day;
But why are both grannies crying?
And *what* did Uncle Jim say?

The vicar was very boring,
At least, that's what our dad said.
Mum said dad should have whispered,
And belted him right round the head.

My auntie the bride looked so pretty,
It was nice when we had to sing;
But oh, what a commotion!
The best man said he'd lost the ring.

Later, we all had a party,
And my mum and dad had a row.
Both of the grannies were crying,
And one of my grandpas was, now.

Everyone got rather tired,
The food and drink soon were gone,
My flowers were looking wilted,
The day had been very long.

I really loved being a bridesmaid,
It was such a wonderful day.
But I don't think I want to get married . . .
At least, not quite in that way!

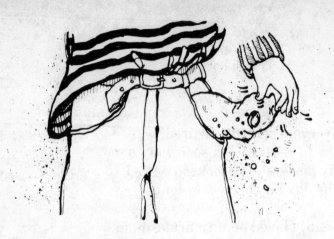

The Sweet

I've found a sweet
In my jeans pocket
It could be a toffee
Or what's left
Of a sherbet rocket

It's all covered
In fluff and other stuff
And stuck to some stones
I found in the street
But it's still a sweet

Scrape off the fluff
And the slime
And all that stuff
Till it looks almost clean

And just
Pop it in

Save Me

Save me from the programmes
That scare me half to death,
And leave me rather sweaty
And feeling out of breath . . .

Save me from the monsters
That are waiting in the gloom,
Hiding in the shadows
All around my room.

Save me from the terrors
That sometimes haunt my dreams,
That chase me through my nightmares
And make me want to scream.

But save me, please, oh save me,
From something worse than this;
Save me from the horrors
Of my granny's slobbery kiss!

The Plaster

I've got a plaster on my knee,
  It's been there several days,
But now it's got to come off,
  At least that's what mum says.

It's looking very dirty
  And the scab will need some air.
The problem is the plaster's stuck
  On lots of little hairs.

I've lifted just one corner,
  And I can't describe the pain;
I really was in agony.
  I won't do that again.

I think I'd better leave it
  For another day or two . . .
What's that, mum? You'll do it now?
  Not likely, no thank you!

What? Rip it off with one quick tug?
    No fear, you must be mad!
Don't touch me, please, just keep away!
    Help me! Save me, dad!

My mum ripped off the plaster,
    And she took the hairs as well.
It didn't really hurt much,
    But I struggled and I fell.

I fell down with a mighty crash,
    And now, unfortunately,
I've got to have a plaster . . .
    On my other knee!

Just Dad

When my big sister
Gets told off
She tosses her hair
And flounces up the stairs.
Then with a BANG!
Her door goes SLAM!

My dad calls her . . . The Flouncer.

When my little sister
Comes out of school
She runs around
And acts the fool.
She bounces and jiggles
And wriggles and giggles.

My dad calls her . . . The Bouncer.

When my mum
Loses her temper
She screams and she shouts
And throws things about.
She says we're all bad
And driving her mad.

My dad calls her . . . The Screamer.

When my other sister
Goes into a dream
When she's drifting and mopy
And acting so dopy,
And spends several days
In a soft, dreamy haze . . .

My dad calls her . . . The Dreamer.

And when sometimes
I do what I shouldn't
Like come home late
Or swing on the gate,
Or slide down the stairs
Or pull someone's hair . . .

My dad calls me . . . The Really Bad Lad.

And what about him?
When he's asleep
In his favourite chair
What's left of his hair
Standing upright,
Mouth open . . . what a sight!

We just call him . . . Dad.

Fathers are Quite Important

When dad woke up this morning,
He acted rather strange;
He chuckled, and he smiled a lot
(At least that made a change).

At breakfast he kept looking
Under all the plates,
And then he said he understood
Why we should make him wait.

By lunchtime dad was grumpy,
He said, 'A joke's a joke.
I like you kids to have a laugh,
I'm quite a decent bloke.'

What could he mean? we wondered,
What was he on about?
And why was our dad cross now?
Why did he start to shout?

'Fathers are quite important,
Dads are nice!' he said.
We'd hardly time to say, 'Quite right!'
Before he'd gone to bed.

We wondered, and we wondered,
Why dad had been that way.
You don't think . . . it couldn't, could it?
Have been . . . Father's Day?

Grrrrrr . . .

Sometimes

When I'm walking
Down the street
I look at my feet

Grr . . .

And imagine how I'd feel
With big, sharp claws
On the end of my paws

Grrrrr . . .

And hot, yellow eyes
To seek out my prey;
It won't get away!

Grrrrrrrrr . . .

And a long, strong tail
Flicking behind on the trail;
But what's this? There's fur

Grrrrrrrrrrrrr . . .

Grrrrrowing all over me,
I'm grrrrrowling and prowling
And . . .

Grrrrrrrrrrrrrrrrr!
GRRRRRRRRRRRRRRRRRRRR!!
GRRRRRRRRRRRRRRRRRRRRRRRR!!!

Sniff

My name is (sniff)
Samantha (sniff)
And I have (sniff)
A problem (sniff sniff)

My mum (sniff)
Says I (sniff)
Sniff (sniff)
All the time (sniff sniff)

If I don't (sniff)
Stop sniffing (sniff)
She says (sniff)
She'll put a peg on my nose (sniff sniff)

She says (sniff)
I should have (sniff)
A hanky (sniff)
And blow it (sniff)

I say (sniff)
I know it (sniff)
But I can't (sniff)
Do it (sniff sniff)

And she (sniff)
Says that's (sniff)
A load of (sniff)
Piffle (sniff sniff)

So I (sniff)
Suppose (sniff)
I'd better try (sniff)
To blow my nose (sniff sniff)

But (sniff)
I'd rather (sniff sniff)
Sniff (sniff sniff sniff)
And sniffle (sniff sniff sniff sniff)

31

Clever Clogs

I'm too clever by half
My mates all say

I'm so sharp I'll cut myself
They said the other day

My hand goes shooting up
I'm nearly always first

I'm so full of the answers
I just might burst

My mates call me clever clogs
And they make fun of me

They call me teacher's pet
And sneer continually

I could keep my mouth shut
Not put my hand up ever

Maybe that's the answer . . .
I hate being clever

Friends

I'm only little
You're very big
I eat like a mouse
You eat like a pig

But we're friends, just the same

I like it quiet
You like it LOUD
I like to be alone sometimes
You're always in a crowd

But we're friends, just the same

I have seven brothers
You've just got your mum
You're not afraid of anything
I still suck my thumb

But we're friends, just the same

I'm good with numbers
You're good with words
I don't know any funny jokes
Yours are the best I've heard

But we're friends, just the same

People think it's funny
They think we're very strange
They say it won't be very long
Before our feelings change

But we're friends, just the same

The New Girl

A new girl started
In our class today.
She didn't look like
Any of us.
Her clothes were . . . different.
She smelled . . . different.
We couldn't understand
The way she talked,
And she couldn't understand
What we said to her.
She had different sorts
Of food in her lunchbox.
Everything about her
Was strange.
No one played with her
At break, and she sat

      Alone

In the corner
Of the playground.
We looked at her
Occasionally, at her
Different hair, her
Different bag, her
Different shoes.
Everything about her
Was strange . . .
Except how,
when home-time came,
she ran to her mother
and held her very, very

tight

My Friend Edward Cole

My friend Edward Cole says:
He's allowed to stay up till midnight.

But I don't believe him.

My friend Edward Cole says:
He's got his very own television.

But I don't believe him.

My friend Edward Cole says:
He gets £25 a week pocket money.

But I don't believe him.

My friend Edward Cole says:
His dad's got a million pounds.

But I don't believe him.

My friend Edward Cole says:
He can do black-belt karate.

But I don't believe him.

My friend Edward Cole says:
He's been in an alien spaceship.

But I don't believe him.

My friend Edward Cole says:
He's told so many lies today
His mum won't let him out to play.

I believe him, I believe him!

Round Our Table

Round our table
Sam is in love
With Anthea

But Anthea
Is in love
With Clint

Clint is
Almost in love
With Tracey

But doesn't
Really like
Her squint

That just
Leaves me
And I'm

In a bit
Of a jam
I sit next

To Anthea
And I'm (choke,
Sob, howl)

in love
With
Sam

The Street in Winter

The street is
cold today,

shrunk in on itself,
wet from overnight
rain, and dark

under a low,
grey sky. Hugging

itself for warmth,
it pulls some fog
round its shoulders

like a thin
winter coat.

A Message

Hello
         feet
You're a
         long
         way
         away
And the
         distance
         between   us
Grows   each   day
If you can hear me
Wiggle those toes
Can you see the spot
On my
         nose?
You'll never know
         feet
Just how fond I am of you
Down
         There

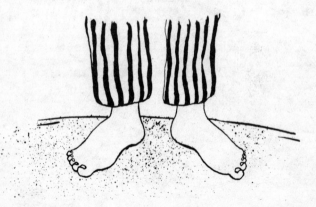

The Street in Summer

The street looks
Hot today,

Relaxed, face up
To the warm,
Blue sky,

In no hurry
To go anywhere,
Basking in

The sunshine.
The soft breeze
Rustling the leaves

Is like

A sigh

Rain

We couldn't go out to play
At morning break today.

The sky was dark and rain
Came down in big drops to stain

The playground. Then lightning flashed,
And suddenly the thunder crashed

And made us jump. It was so loud
It seemed as if, behind a cloud,

A giant mirror had been smashed.
The thunder rumbled, lightning flashed

Again, and we just watched the rain,
Safe and dry behind the windowpanes.

Later, at home-time, we walked round
Pieces of the mirror on the ground.

They lay there, reflecting the sky,
And all the children going by.

It's All Decided

Right, it's all decided then,
It's spaceships that we'll play.
I'm the captain, you're the crew,
And you do what I say.

I'll wear the space-suit,
You can sit back there,
And when I give the order . . .
Pretend there is no air.

You're gasping and you're choking,
And soon you'll be quite dead.
I'll just blast off for Mars, now.
What was that you said?

You'd rather be the captain?
You want to be the hero?
I'm sorry, there's no time to talk,
The countdown's reaching zero.

I'm sorry, I just don't agree,
You're not the hero sort.
Now can we keep on counting?
It's time to leave spaceport.

Oh . . . you say you're leaving?
And you want *your* space-suit, too?
But how can I be captain
If I haven't got a crew?

Right, it's all decided then,
I'm the crew and you're in charge . . .
Look out! A meteor's coming,
Hot and fast and very large . . .

It's crashed into the spaceship . . .
You're wounded . . . now you're dead.
I'll have to save us! Where's the suit?
What was that you said?

There's Nobody Quite Like Me

My friend Charlotte and I
Are exactly the same height.

But there's nobody quite like me.

My friend Samantha and I
Have exactly the same sort of hair.

But there's nobody quite like me.

My friend Tracey and I
Have exactly the same colour eyes.

But there's nobody quite like me.

My friend Lisa and I
Always get exactly the same marks.

But there's nobody quite like me.

My friend Andrea and I
Like exactly the same records.

But there's nobody quite like me.

My twin sister and I
Look exactly alike, everyone says.

But there's nobody, nobody quite like me!

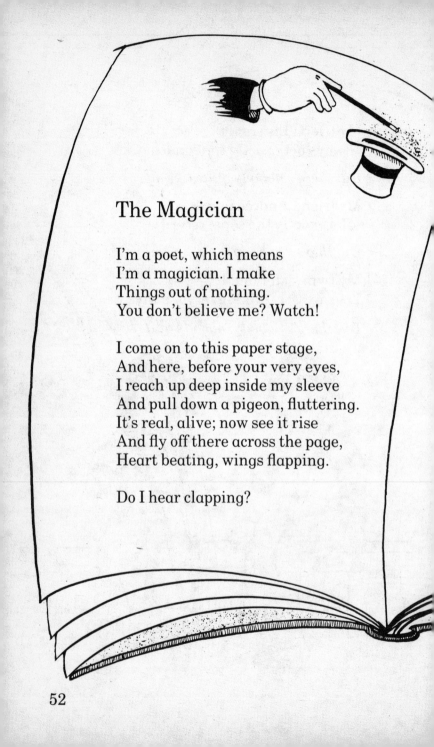

The Magician

I'm a poet, which means
I'm a magician. I make
Things out of nothing.
You don't believe me? Watch!

I come on to this paper stage,
And here, before your very eyes,
I reach up deep inside my sleeve
And pull down a pigeon, fluttering.
It's real, alive; now see it rise
And fly off there across the page,
Heart beating, wings flapping.

Do I hear clapping?

As you read this A poem may be slipping through your eyes And into your mind

Escape

Some of the poems
In this book
Have formed
An escape committee

A tunnel has been dug
Through the pages
And poems have escaped

Even now
As you read this
A poem may
Be slipping
Through your eyes
And into your mind

In

Disguise

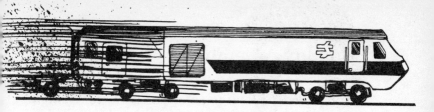

Can I Come Along?

Train, train,
rattling along,
where are you going to?
Can I come along?

From station to station,
From coast to coast,
where do you like going
the most?

Train, train,
thundering along,
where are you going to?
Can I come along?

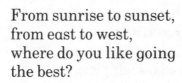

From sunrise to sunset,
from east to west,
where do you like going
the best?

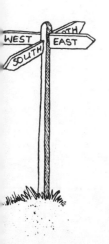

Train, train,
whistling along –
where are you going to?
Where have you gone?

Monday Assembly

(For Stewart Fleming Infant and Junior School)

Three hundred children
File into the hall,
Some of them are very big,
Some are very small.

Some of them are yawning,
Some are looking bright;
Some of them are black or brown,
Some of them are white.

Some of them are messy,
Some of them are neat;
Some are good at football,
Some have two left feet.

Some are very brainy,
And always pass their tests;
Others find them very hard,
But try to do their best.

Some are very happy.
One or two are sad.
Most live with both parents,
Some with mum or dad.

Some of them are dreaming
Of what they'd like to be;
Rich, or someone's best friend,
Or starring on TV.

Now the head is talking,
She's telling them what's what.
Some of them are listening,
Some of them are not.

And now the head is saying
It's time to sing a hymn.
'All together, now!' she says.
'One, two, three – begin!'

All of them are singing,
The hymn leads them along;
Three hundred voices,
Singing the same song.

Three hundred voices,
And each one is unique.
But they all blend together
As our school starts the week!

Two Cats

Two cats sitting
On my wall;
One big and mean,
One quite small.

Big cat growls,
Lunges, hisses,
Green eyes flashing –
Big cat misses.

Big cat totters
On my wall;
Paws slip off,
Big cat falls.

One cat sitting,
On my wall;
One cat smiling,
Though he's small.

The Wall

Once, in our playground,
We had a wall.
It was low, with steps,
And really quite small.

But now it isn't there at all.

The teachers said it had to go.
One of them tripped
Over it in the snow.
He said some bad things about our wall.

And now it isn't there at all.

It was great to play on,
When it was cold or
When the sun shone.
I spent part of every day on
Our playground wall.

But now it isn't there at all.

We used to climb on it,
And have a good time on it,
And say, '*I'm* the king
Of the castle now!'
On our good old wall.

And now it isn't there at all.

We always used to hide behind it.
Even in the fog we'd find it.
And I really wouldn't mind it
Being built again. I'd like it back,
Our playground wall.

For now it isn't there at all.

Where it was there's
Just some air.
We call that spot:

The wall that isn't there.

Skipping Rhyme

Skipping in the playground
One two three
Here comes a boy
Will you marry me?

Skipping in the playground
Four five six
Here comes a boy
With legs like sticks!

Skipping in the playground
Seven eight nine
Here comes a boy . . .
This one's mine!

Skipping in the playground
We've reached ten
There go the boys
Let's start again!

Whispers

Hisssssssssssssss . . .

Whispers in the playground
Hissing as they slide
Slithering up and into ears
Hear them slip and glide

Sarah's next to Lucy
Whispers soft and low
Now Lucy's spreading whispers
Listen, hear them go . . .

Stephen's spotted Tracey
He's whispered to her twice
He's whispering and whispering
Tracey thinks it's nice

Hissing in the schoolyard
Sounds like slithery snakes
Whispers hissing as they slide
Hear the noise they make

Justin's telling Susan
Something that she hates
And Sam has sent a whisper
Slithering out the gate

Whispers in the playground
Sliding round our feet
Sliding through the classrooms
Whispers in the street

Hissing in the schoolyard
A nest of coiling snakes
Whispers hissing as they slide . . .
Hear the noise they make

Hisssssssssssssss . . .

65

The Footballer

I take the pass
In the crowded
Playground
And kill it
The ball's tamed
By my foot
And goes where
I will it
To go

And maybe
I'll take a shot
From here
My view is clear
Through to
The coats we
Use as posts

I take off
Slow, slide round
The tacklers
Past the skipping
Girls, dodge
The dinner ladies
Whirl on my heel

Draw back
A foot and SHOOT!
Through the hole . . .
GOAL!
The playground
Fades away . . .
This is Wembley
On Cup Final Day

Football

Playing football
Can be fun,
Whoops! They've scored,
That's number one.

Come on, Pete, you're
Almost through!
Whoops! They've scored,
That's number two.

We're moving now,
Pass to me!
Whoops! They've scored,
That's number three.

Oww! I've fallen,
My knee's sore.
Whoops! They've scored,
That's number four.

Come on lads,
Where's your drive?
Whoops! They've scored,
That's number five.

That makes six . . .
Seven . . . wait!
We've nearly scored!
They've got number eight.

Football's boring
Played this way.
Er . . . please, miss,
Is it the end of play?

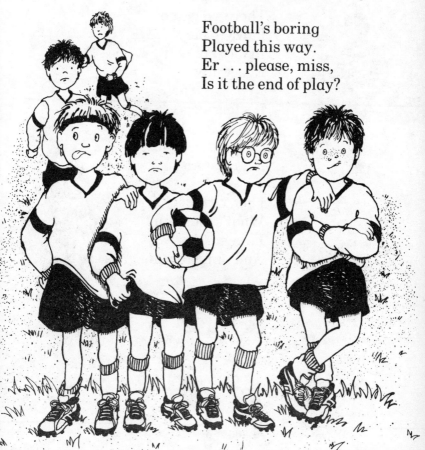

Kiss Chase

There's a game
I love to play
In fact I play it
Every day

It's terrific,
It goes like this:
Chase chase chase
Kiss kiss kiss

I don't know
What's more fun
I like to kiss
And I like to run

It's fantastic,
It goes like this:
Chase chase chase
Kiss kiss kiss

Hear our footsteps
Pounding round
Hear those kisses
What a sound

What a game!
It goes like this:
Chase chase chase
Kiss kiss kiss

Ssssh . . .

Ssssh . . .

Come a little closer . . .
I've got a secret
You won't have heard

Ssssh . . .

You promise not
To tell? Well . . .
Come a little closer . . .

Ssssh . . .

I don't know where
To start . . . Cross
Your heart you won't . . .

Ssssh . . .

OK, but promise
You won't tell Lee?
Or Sarah? Or even Sam?

Ssssh . . .

Well . . . you won't believe
This . . . whisper, whisper,
Whisper, sssssssssss . . .

What? *What?*

Well! That's completely
Absurd. What do you mean,
You've already heard?

73

Stop the Slobbering

I hate it
When people kiss
On the telly

It's all
Slobbering and slurping
And silly words

It's worse
Than watching
My big sister

And her
Smelly boyfriend . . .
They kiss

All the time . . .
Mum laughs when
I complain

Kissing's no
crime, she says
It's great

Well it
Should be banned
On the telly,

I say,
And especially banned
By our front gate

Slow Eating

My sister
Is the slowest eater
You've ever seen

By the time I've finished
My dinner and I'm ready
To start my ice-cream

She's only just
Picked up
Her knife and fork

Mum says
It's because she doesn't eat
She just talks

The trouble is
We all have to wait
For our ice-cream

Until she's
Cleared her plate
Of every bit and stalk

But she just talks
And talks and talks and talks . . .
And talks and talks . . .

Parentspeak

If I've told you
A thousand times
I've told you once
Don't gobble your food
Think yourself lucky
There are people starving
How often must I tell you
Mark my words
Don't slam that door
Isn't it time you were asleep
Why won't you ever
Get out of bed?
What was that you said?

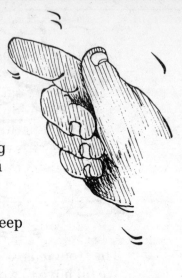

Why must you argue?
Children should
Be seen and not heard
When I was your age
I wouldn't have dared
There's no such
thing as can't
I can't believe what
I'm hearing
Don't say 'ain't' or 'innit'
I'll give you your
Pocket money
In a minute, in a minute

Have you done
Your homework?
I haven't got a clue
You shouldn't be listening
It's got nothing
To do with you
You don't own the
Television, I pay the bills
What did your last
Servant die of?
Come on, we haven't
Got all year . . . I've told
You a thousand times
It'll all end in tears . . .

The Perfect Answer

My little brother
Can be horrible . . .

Dad said to him
The other day,
'Thomas, you're
The most argumentative
Little boy in
The whole world.'

'No I'm not,'
He said.

Then he

Simply

Walked

Away

Flats

I've always wanted to live in a house
  with stairs
I've always lived in flats
  and that's
What I don't like about them
  they're flat
And you can never get away from
  your mum
Or your sister and her boyfriend
  or your
Little brother and his mates they're
  always squeezed
Into the front room all together with
  the fire
On breathing each other's air
  if I
Lived in a house with stairs
  I could
Get away

up there

81

It Wasn't Me

Dad, you know that broken glass
Lying on the kitchen floor?
The one that's in a puddle,
Right there by the door?

Well, it wasn't me that did it.

Mum, you know my little brother,
The one who tells those lies?
The one who always blames me
When he's hurt himself and cries?

Well, it wasn't me that did it.

Dad, you know those new school shoes,
The ones that were so tough?
The ones that really cost a lot?
They weren't quite tough enough.

But it wasn't me that did it.

Mum, you know that little jug
Our dad's mum gave to you?
The one that's on the dresser?
Well, now it's cracked in two.

But it wasn't me that did it.

Dad, you know that broken glass
Lying on the kitchen floor?
The one that's in a puddle,
Right there by the door?

Well . . . that's right, how did you know?
It wasn't me that did it (honest!).

The Ghost of Classroom Three

Something
ectoplasmic →

There's a tapping at the window,
A moaning at the door,
And something ectoplasmic
Sticking to the floor . . .

But don't panic, don't be frightened
By anything you see,
It's really nothing special,
Just the ghost of classroom three.

POOF!

It doesn't come out often,
Maybe once or twice a year.
It wanders round and mutters,
Then . . . poof! It disappears.

Sometimes it sits at the desk
Marking books continually . . .
But it's really nothing special,
Just the ghost of classroom three.

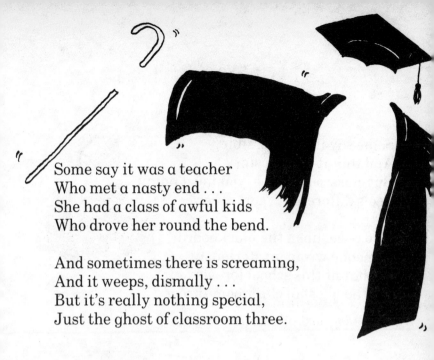

Some say it was a teacher
Who met a nasty end . . .
She had a class of awful kids
Who drove her round the bend.

And sometimes there is screaming,
And it weeps, dismally . . .
But it's really nothing special,
Just the ghost of classroom three.

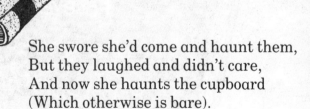

She swore she'd come and haunt them,
But they laughed and didn't care,
And now she haunts the cupboard
(Which otherwise is bare).

And sometimes there are others,
A whole classful you can see.
Doing endless homework
For the ghost of classroom three.

Some say it isn't possible,
And that it's just a story . . .
But classroom three, you must admit,
Feels different . . . sort of *eerie*.

And once, upon the blackboard
Someone wrote mysteriously,
'I'll haunt this school forever . . .
I'm the ghost of classroom three.'

There's a rapping on the desk tops,
There's a rattling at the door,
And something trying to get out
Of teacher's locked desk drawer . . .

But don't panic, don't be frightened,
Don't scare too easily;
It's really nothing special;
Just the ghost of classroom three . . .

87

The Wilderness

Sometimes when I'm
In the park,
In the hour before
It gets dark;

Down by the pond
And the little stream,
The park stops being
What it seems.

That line of trees,
That tangled bush . . .
It's a wilderness,
Strange and hushed.

I'm an explorer,
All alone,
Ten thousand miles
From my home . . .

Wondering what
I'll find out there –
Treasure? Cannibals?
Do I dare

To break from cover,
Follow those tracks?
I must go on,
Can't turn back . . .

A wolf is howling,
Should I wait?
It's nearly dark . . .
And there's the gate.

Down by the pond
And the little stream,
Darkness settles
On my dream.

At home I sit
And watch TV,
But in my head
There's another me.

Out in the wilderness,
All alone,
Ten thousand miles
From my home.

In the Garden

From my window
I could see
Our old brown dog
Patiently

Watching ...

Next door's cat
Who, stomach down,
Tail out flat
Sat and sat and sat

Watching ...

One small bird
A sharp-beaked thrush
Who, head askew
Stood there, hushed

Watching ...

A tiny worm
Who, unaware,
Wriggled and squirmed
Beneath her stare ...

Real Birds

We've got a bird table
In our garden

All sorts of birds
Fly down to nibble nuts
And peck at crusts

But they don't look
Real to me
At least, not as real
As the birds
In the wildlife
Programmes on TV

They fly about
And I can't follow them
There's no slow motion
No freeze-frame
No camera waiting
Like a cat
To swallow them

And so I watch
The birds
On our bird table
And wonder what's
More real . . .

The birds I can see?
Or the birds on TV?

There's a Murmur

(A summer drama)

There's a murmur
In the garden
It's the sound
Of several bees
Humming there
And buzzing
Around our
Apple tree

There's a murmur
In the garden
It's the sound
Of granny's snores
She's lying
In a deck chair
(And she's showing
Us her drawers)

There's a murmur
In the garden
It's the bees
They're getting close
Getting near
Her mouth now . . .
One's landed
On her nose

There's a silence
In the garden
We're all waiting
Holding breath . . .
Will the bee
Sting granny?
We're all scared
To death . . .

There's a murmur
In the garden
It's the sound
Of one small bee
Leaving granny's
Snoring face
Settling on
Her knee

There's a murmur
In the garden
It's granny
Dreaming dreams
She's brushing
Bees off knees now . . .
It makes us
Want to scream!

There's a yawning
In the garden
And all the bees
Have gone . . .
Granny's waking
Up now –
'Have I been
Sleeping long?'

I Like It That Way

Our house isn't in
The best part of town

I like it that way

It's got tiles missing,
And the fence is falling down

I like it that way

It's not very big
It's really quite small

I like it that way

98

The wallpaper's peeling
And there's cracks in the walls

I like it that way

It's got a great garden
With a really big tree

I like it that way

It's the place I was born;
Where I can be . . . *me*

I like it that way

The Picture

There's a picture that my dad's got,
    He keeps it by his bed,
Of him when he was little,
    With my grandpa, who's dead.

They're standing close together,
    On a day out at the fair;
Grandpa's got his arm round dad.
    There's no one else there.

Both of them are smiling,
    And looking straight ahead;
My dad with his father,
    With my grandpa, who's dead.

I never knew my grandpa,
    And he never knew of me,
But even though we didn't meet
    We're still family.

Dad looks just like grandpa,
    And I'm like dad, mum said;
Which means I look like grandpa,
    My grandpa, who's dead.

They're happy in that picture,
  On a day out at the fair;
And I know it's strange to say it,
  But I wish that I'd been there.

There before the camera,
  Looking straight ahead,
With my dad when he was little,
  And my grandpa, who's dead.

Busy Week

On Mondays
  It's my Brownie night
On Tuesdays
  I do gym
On Wednesdays
  I do ballet
On Thursday nights
  I swim
On Fridays
  I do gym again
On Saturdays
  I sleep late . . .
On Sundays
  I just wish the week
  Wasn't seven days . . .
  But eight!

June

1	Thurs	Swimming - Test
2	Fri	gym
3	Sat	
4	Sun	Tea at Grans
5	Mon	Brownies
6	Tues	gym
7	Wed	Ballet - don't forget tights
8	Thurs	Swimming
9	Fri	gym
10	Sat	(Mums Birthday)
11	Sun	Tracy coming to stay ✳
12	Mon	Brownies badge night
13	Tues	gym
14	Wed	Ballet
15	Thurs	Swimming PAST Test
16	Fri	gym
17	Sat	Shopping mum
18	Sun	Fête
19	Mon	Brownies — Cooking
20	Tues	gym
21	Wed	Ballet - concert practice
22	Thurs	Swimming - up to group I
23	Fri	gym
24	Sat	Brownie Jumble Sale.
25	Sun	grandpa + Gran coming
26	Mon	Brownies
27	Tues	gym
28	Wed	Ballet - remember costume
29	Thurs	swimming - diving
30	Fri	gym

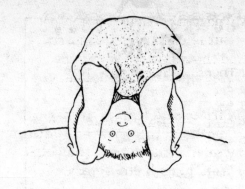

My Little Brother

My mother had a baby,
    And my friends were quick to say,
'That's the end of all your fun –
    You won't forget this day.'

They said he'd be a nuisance,
    He'd be a smelly pest,
He'd tire out my mum and dad . . .
    Oh, I forget the rest.

It's turned out very different;
    It wasn't lots of bother.
In fact, the truth is simple:
    I *like* my little brother.

He's lots of fun to play with,
    He crawls about and smiles.
I like to take him to the park
    And push him round for miles.

My parents do look tired,
    But I haven't been ignored,
And though we're very busy,
    We're never, ever bored.

My friends all think I'm stupid,
    That something's wrong with me;
Boys don't like babies, they all say.
    Well, I think differently.

I don't care what my friends think,
    Or say to one another;
I'm glad mum had our baby –
    I *like* my little brother.

Dark

I'm not scared
Of many things;
But I don't like
the dark.

It's always there,
Inside boxes, waiting
To get out,
Waiting patiently
For the day to go
So it can seep down
From the sky;
It's there,
Under my bed, waiting
For me to turn out
The light
So it can jump out
And frighten me . . .

It even follows
Me around,

Darkly
Copying
My shape

Without

A sound

The Dream

I had a dream
I dreamed it was
An ordinary day

I dreamed I woke up
And did ordinary things
In an ordinary way

All my family
Were there as usual
And I went to school

Where I did all
The ordinary things
I do as a rule

I came home
I watched the telly
I had my usual tea

In my dream
I went to bed
The way I do usually

In bed I dreamed . . .
I mean, I dreamed
I dreamed a dream

And then I woke up . . .
I mean, I dreamed
I woke up from that dream

Now I don't know
Where my dreams end
And life begins

This could
All be a dream
I might be in

The Uninvited Guest

I went to a fancy-dress party,
  And all my friends were there;
Two done up as vampires,
  One dressed as a bear.

Neil was being Superman,
  Tracey was a stone,
Sarah was a rubbish bin –
  We all left her alone.

Tony was a Frankenstein,
  His teeth and eyes were red.
'What an ugly mask!' we shouted . . .
  'But it's my face,' he said.

Everyone was having fun,
  We played games on the floor . . .
Neil was winning, then we heard
  A knocking on the door.

Someone coming to the party,
   Someone coming late.
He certainly had a costume on,
   Although it looked a state.

He seemed to be an alien,
   With lots of bulging eyes.
But those tentacles looked terrible.
   He'd never win a prize.

He sat right next to Sarah,
   Despite the awful smell,
Then ate a plate of sausages,
   And fourteen cakes, as well.

He ate a plate of sausage rolls,
   And then he couldn't wait . . .
He ate the ice cream in the fridge,
   And then he ate . . . a plate!

111

The party soon was over,
    Our mums and dads arrived,
All complaining of the thing
    Blocking up the drive.

It was some sort of vehicle,
    With red lights all around.
It had no wheels but sat there,
    Just above the ground . . .

But Neil had lost his special hat,
    And Tracey fought with Lee.
Sarah didn't want to go,
    And turned on the TV.

No one really listened
   When a man on TV said
That something had been spotted,
   Something fast, and red . . .

By the time we got outside,
   The vehicle thing had gone.
Where it had sat there was a hole
   As deep as it was long.

No one took much notice;
   We all went on our way . . .
And who *was* that dressed as an alien?
   Who invited him, anyway?

I'd Like to be a Spaceman

I'd like to be a spaceman
    Zooming through the stars,
I'd visit lots of planets
    Like Jupiter and Mars.

I'd like to roam the spaceways
    Where no one's ever been,
Where planets orbit double suns
    And where the skies are green.

I'd walk in alien jungles,
    On beaches wild and free,
And where the only footprints
    Are those made by me.

I'd see the strangest deserts,
    And maybe in the sands
I'd find a ruined city
    Raised by alien hands.

I'd find a thousand treasures,
    And then perhaps one day,
I'd meet a fellow traveller
    In the Milky Way.

An alien from a planet
    In a distant galaxy,
Roaming through the spaceways . . .
    Just like me.

Christmas is Coming

Christmas is coming
I can hear wishes
Turning into lists of presents

Jingle bells, jingle bells, jingle . . .

Christmas is coming
There's a tree in our front room
Collecting tinsel and lights

Jingle bells, jingle bells, jingle . . .

Christmas is coming
I can smell mince pies
And puddings cooking themselves

Jingle bells, jingle bells, jingle . . .

Christmas is coming
Gangs of wrapped presents
Are gathering all over the world

Jingle bells, jingle bells, jingle . . .

Christmas is coming
It's coming down our street
Round the corner and up our path . . .

IT'S HERE!

Jingle bells, jingle bells, jingle . . .
All the way, oh what fun . . .

How to Open Your Christmas Presents: Two Views

One

It's best to go
As slowly as you can.
Take plenty of time,
To arrange your presents
In neat piles
While everyone else is
Ripping theirs apart . . .
And then start only
When they've all finished.
Go very, very, very slowly . . .
Peel back the sellotape
Without tearing the paper,
Peek under the wrapping
Every so often,
And slide it off very, very,
Very slowly . . .
Smile a lot.
Don't worry if it
Takes all day;
It's better that way.

Two

Quick, quick,
Grab those presents
As fast as you can,
Don't, don't, don't wait!
Don't hesitate!
Rip, tear,
Anywhere, who cares
What others think,
And don't worry about
Those slowcoaches who
Take their time . . .
Go very, very, very
Very, very quickly,
Especially if your presents
Are wrapped extra thickly . . .
Remember, you haven't
Got all year . . .
Christmas day's today
And *only* today . . .
It's better that way.

119

The Whatsit

I think I've lost my whatsit,
  The one I got last year,
For Christmas, or my birthday . . .
  It's simply disappeared.

I had it just the other day,
  I put it on the floor;
Or was it in the thingummybob?
  The one behind the door?

I got it from old what's-his-name,
  Or was it from his brother?
It's blue, I think, or maybe red.
  There couldn't be another.

I'm sure I left it somewhere,
  Perhaps it's in the hall . . .
But now I come to think of it,
  It can't be there at all.

I'll have to keep on looking,
  I know it's somewhere near . . .
How can my favourite whatsit
  Have simply disappeared?

Lost

My brother's always
Losing things.

This year so far
(And it's only February)
He's lost a hat,
His gloves and scarf,

Two school books,
His library card,
My best pen,
The football he got
For Christmas,
Dad's watch,
The tin-opener,

The key to the back door,
And (when he had a cold)
His voice.

Mum said he'd probably
Lose himself one day
If he didn't buck his
Ideas up. We all laughed.
By the way, you haven't
Seen him, have you?

I Wish

I wish I was
An only child
No brothers or sisters
To drive me wild

I wish I had
An older brother
And a sister
And another

I hate it when
We have a fight
I'm always wrong
They're always right

I hate it when
There's no one there
To play with me
To laugh, to share

We always have
To be together
Wherever we go
Whatever the weather

I always have
To be alone
To have no one
Be on my own

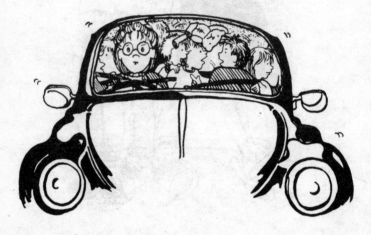

I hate it when
They take my stuff
Sometimes I've just
Had enough

I hate it when
I feel this way
Sometimes I just
Want to say . . .

I wish I was
A different me
In a different
Family

I wish, I wish,
I really do
That you were me
And I were . . . you

127

The Kick

The story begins
With a boy called Paul:
He kicked his sister
In the hall.

She went to school
And kicked poor Kate,
Standing by
The infant gate.

Kate kicked Tracey,
Who kicked Tim;
He kicked Charlotte,
She kicked him.

Tim kicked someone
Else, and then
Charlotte kicked him
Once again.

Tim went off and kicked
His brother,
Who kicked a girl,
And then another.

That one turned
And near the wall,
She kicked a boy
Whose name was . . . Paul.

'Hey!' he said,
'That wasn't fair!'
'Well,' laughed his sister,
'I don't care!'